Goldilocks and the Three Bears

Story retold by Janet Brown
Illustrations by Ken Morton

Colour Library Direct

Three bears live in a house in the middle of the forest. There is a big Daddy Bear, a medium-sized Mummy Bear, and a tiny little Baby Bear.

The three bears eat porridge for breakfast. Most people like their porridge hot. But bears love cold porridge.

Mummy Bear sets the table. Then the family goes for a walk while the porridge cools down.

What do the three bears do while their porridge cools down?

Goldilocks is also walking in the forest. She collects berries and sings to herself. She gathers flowers.

Walking makes her hungry. The warm sun makes her sleepy. She spies a pretty house in the middle of the trees.

“Perhaps I can rest there,” she thinks. “Maybe they will feed me.”

She does not know that this house belongs to the three bears!

Who does the pretty house in the middle of the trees belong to?

Inside, the table is set for three. There are three chairs — one big chair, one medium-sized chair, and one tiny little chair.

On the table there are three bowls of porridge — one big bowl, one medium-sized bowl, and one tiny little bowl.

There are also three spoons, a jug of milk and a jar of honey.

How many places have been set at the table?

Goldilocks climbs into the big chair first. “This chair is too hard!” she says.

She tastes the porridge in the big bowl. “And this porridge is too hot!”

Next she tries the medium-sized chair. “This chair is too soft!” she says.

She tastes the porridge in the medium-sized bowl. “And this porridge is too cold!”

What is wrong with the big chair that Goldilocks climbs into first?

Goldilocks sits down in the tiny little chair. It is very comfortable. She tastes the porridge in the tiny little bowl. It is not too hot and it is not too cold.

“This is just perfect!” says Goldilocks. She eats up every last spoonful of porridge.

But Goldilocks is bigger than Baby Bear. After a while the tiny little chair starts to crack and then it breaks into pieces!

Why does Baby Bear's chair break when Goldilocks sits in it?

Goldilocks is tired. She goes upstairs. She finds three beds — a big bed, a medium-sized bed, and a tiny little bed.

She climbs into the big bed. “This bed is too hard!” she says.

She climbs into the medium-sized bed. “This bed is too soft!” she says.

She climbs into the tiny little bed. It is not too hard and it is not too soft.

“This is just perfect!” says Goldilocks. She falls fast asleep.

Whose bed does Goldilocks fall asleep in?

The bears return from the forest. “What a lovely walk!” says Daddy Bear. “Let’s eat!”

Then he looks at the breakfast table.

“Somebody’s been sitting on my chair!” growls Daddy Bear.

“Somebody’s been sitting on my chair!” frowns Mummy Bear.

“Somebody’s been sitting on my chair!” wails Baby Bear. “And they’ve smashed it all to pieces!”

Why do you think Baby Bear looks so sad in this picture?

They look at the bowls on the table.

“Somebody’s been eating my porridge!” growls Daddy Bear.

“Somebody’s been eating my porridge!” frowns Mummy Bear.

“Somebody’s been eating my porridge!” wails Baby Bear. “And they’ve eaten it all up!”

Whose bowl is empty?

The three bears rush upstairs.
"Somebody's been sleeping in my bed!" roars Daddy Bear. "Somebody's been sleeping in my bed!" cries Mummy Bear. "Somebody's been sleeping in my bed!" yells Baby Bear. "AND SHE'S STILL HERE!"

At that, Goldilocks opens her eyes. She sees three hairy faces looking down at her — a big face, a medium-sized face, and a tiny little face.
"Help!" she cries. She jumps out of bed and runs all the way home.

The bears are surprised. "Was I too loud?" asks Daddy Bear. "Was I too fierce?" asks Baby Bear?
"I'll make some more porridge," says Mummy Bear.
"It's way past breakfast time."

Why does Baby Bear think Goldilocks is running away?

There are eight things wrong with the picture below.
Can you find them?

Answers:

1) Baby Bear sitting on Daddy Bear's chair
2) Heart design on chair instead of diamonds
3) Mummy Bear on roller skates
4) Milk jug handle missing
5) Left arm of chair pointing upwards
6) Flying spoons
7) Picture hanging upside down
8) One carved chair leg